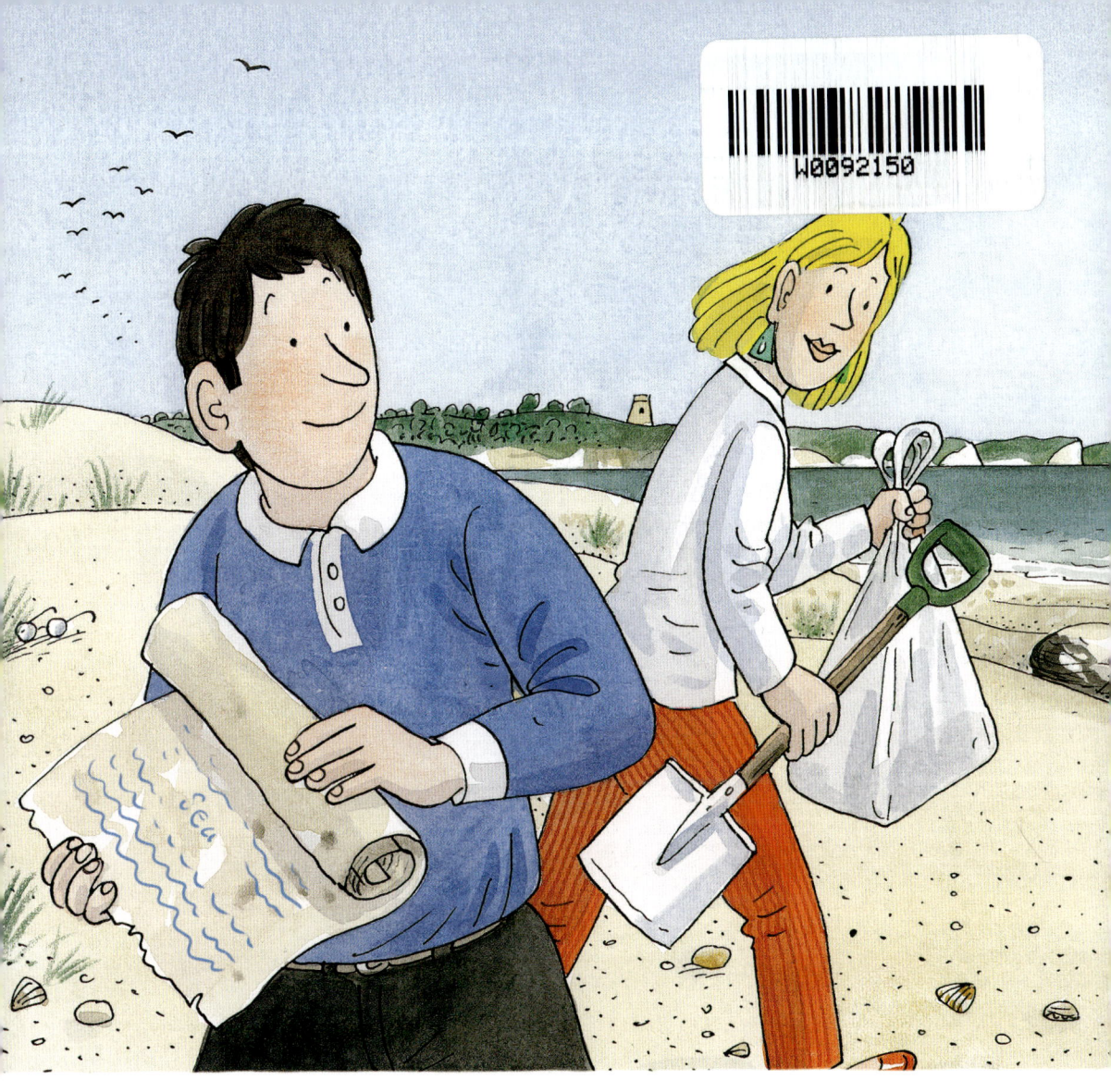

Dad had a map.

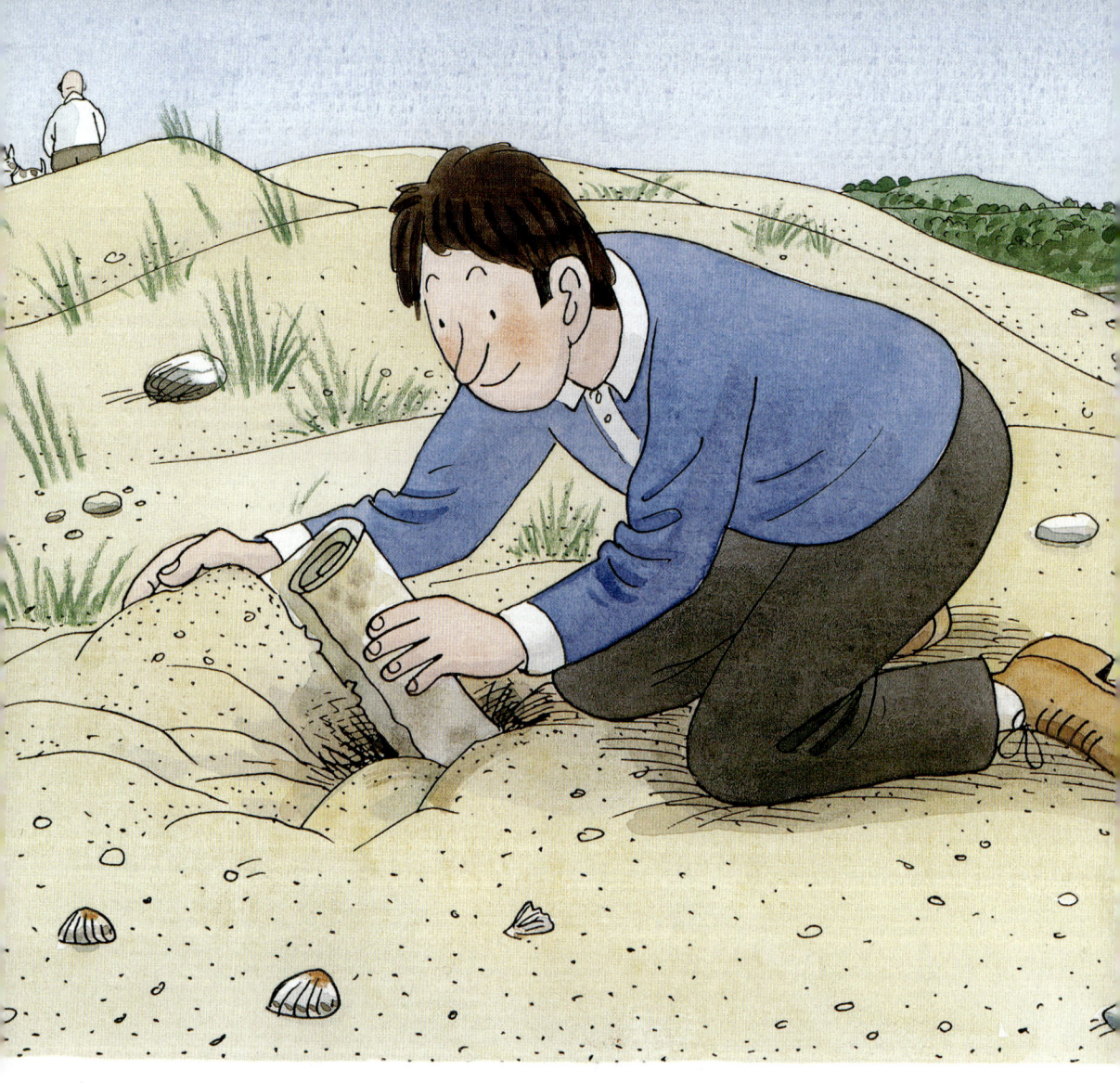

He hid the map in the sand.

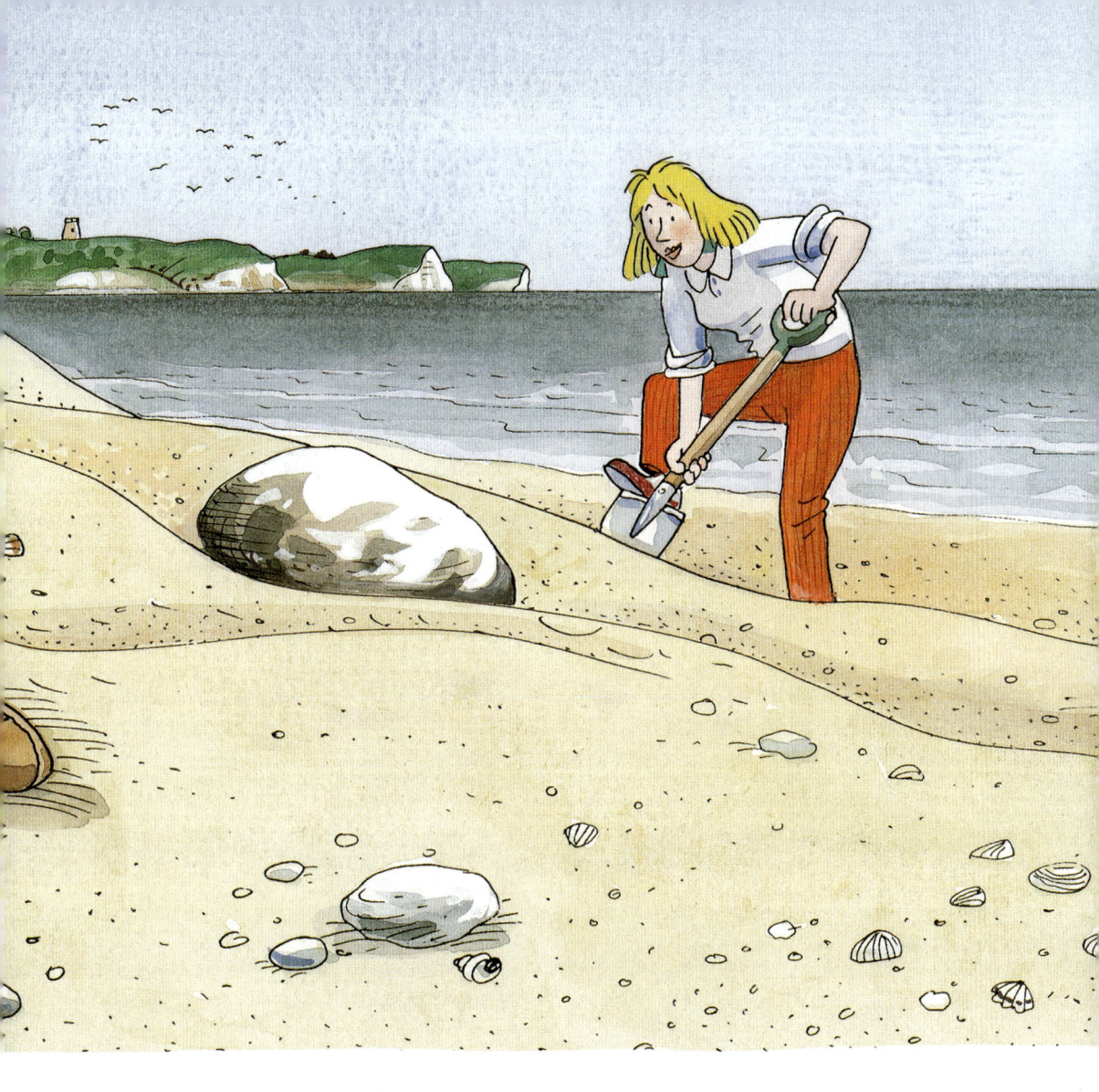

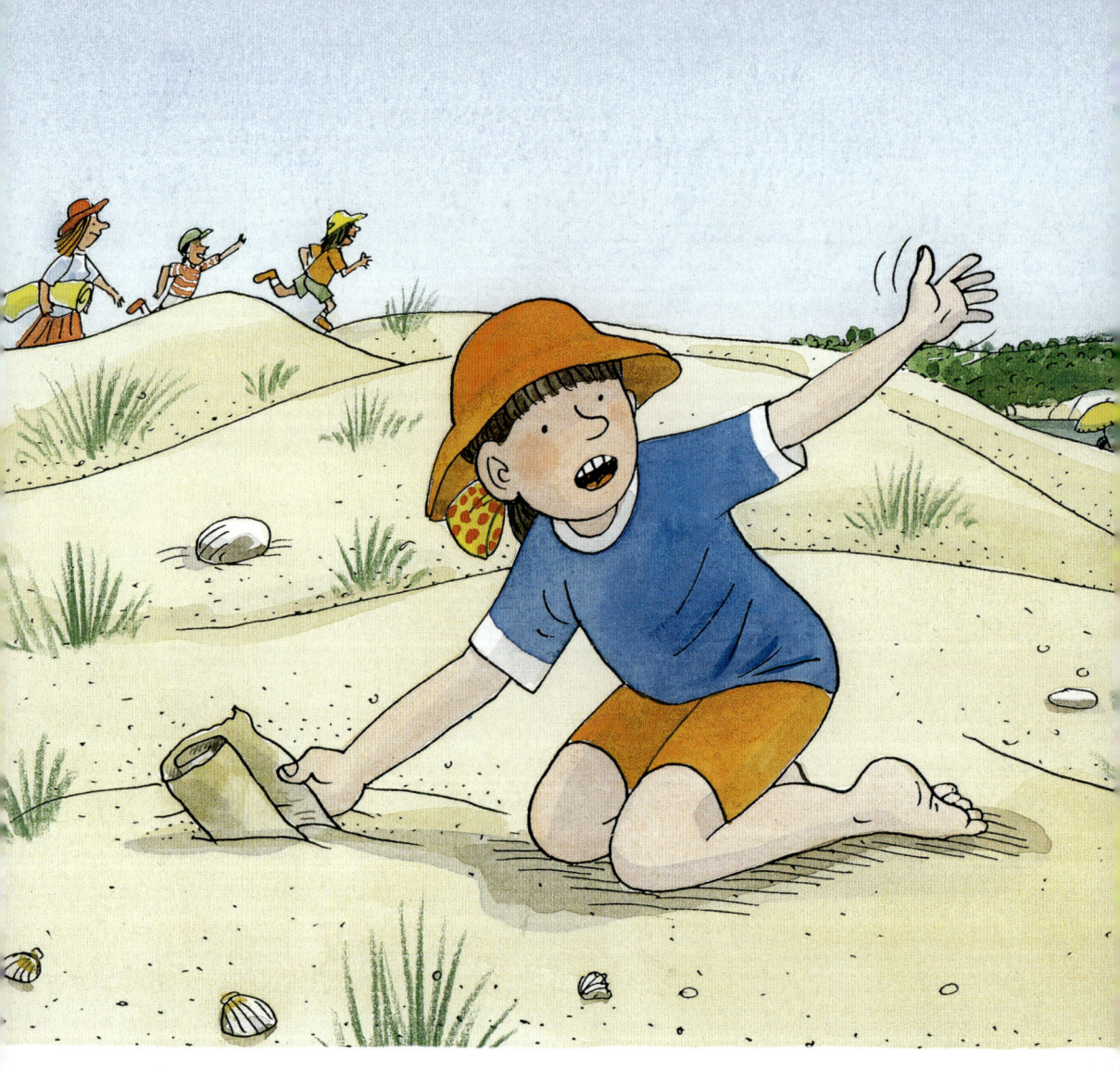

Biff found the map.

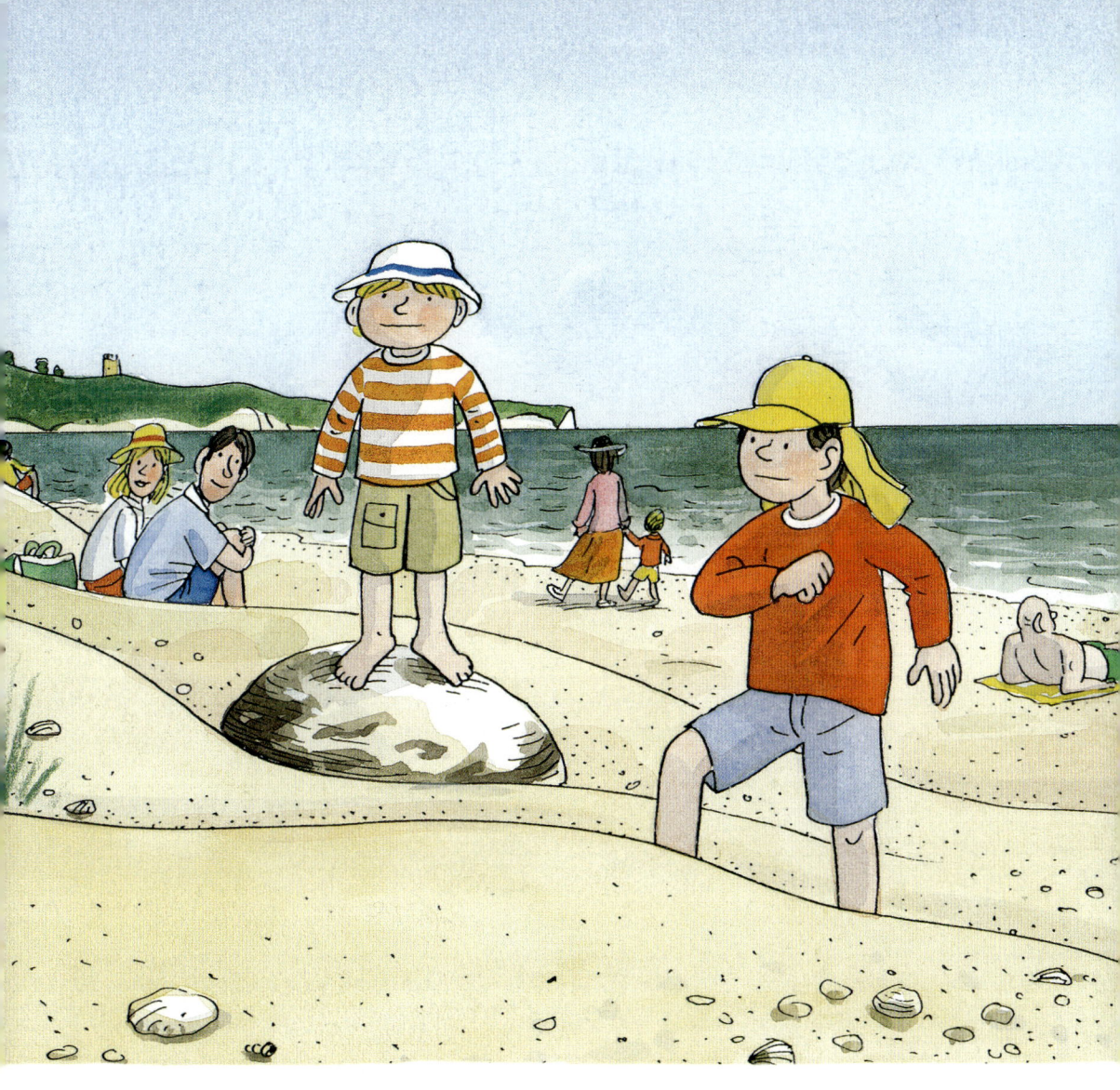

"It is a treasure map," she said.

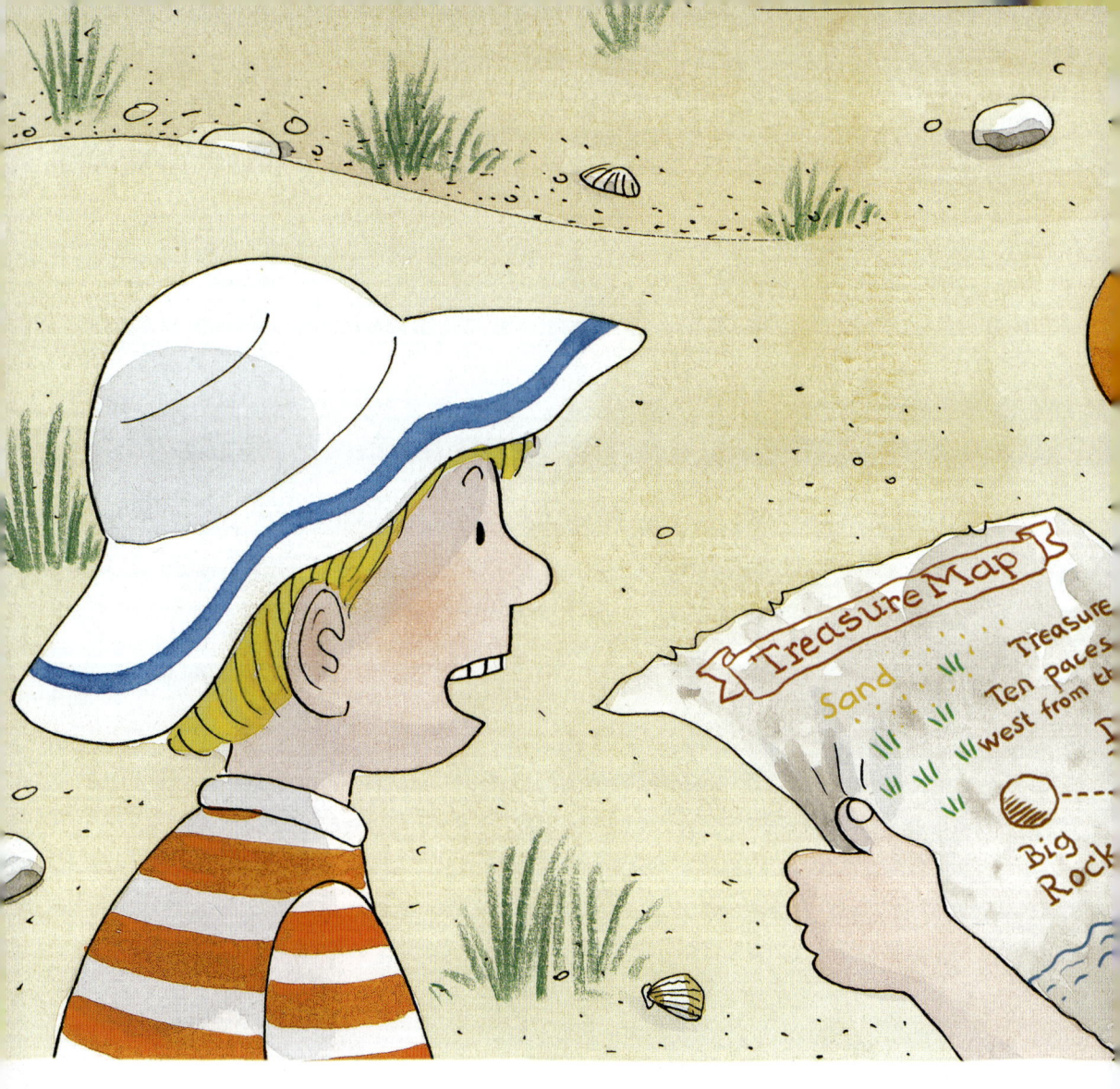

The map said, "Dig here."

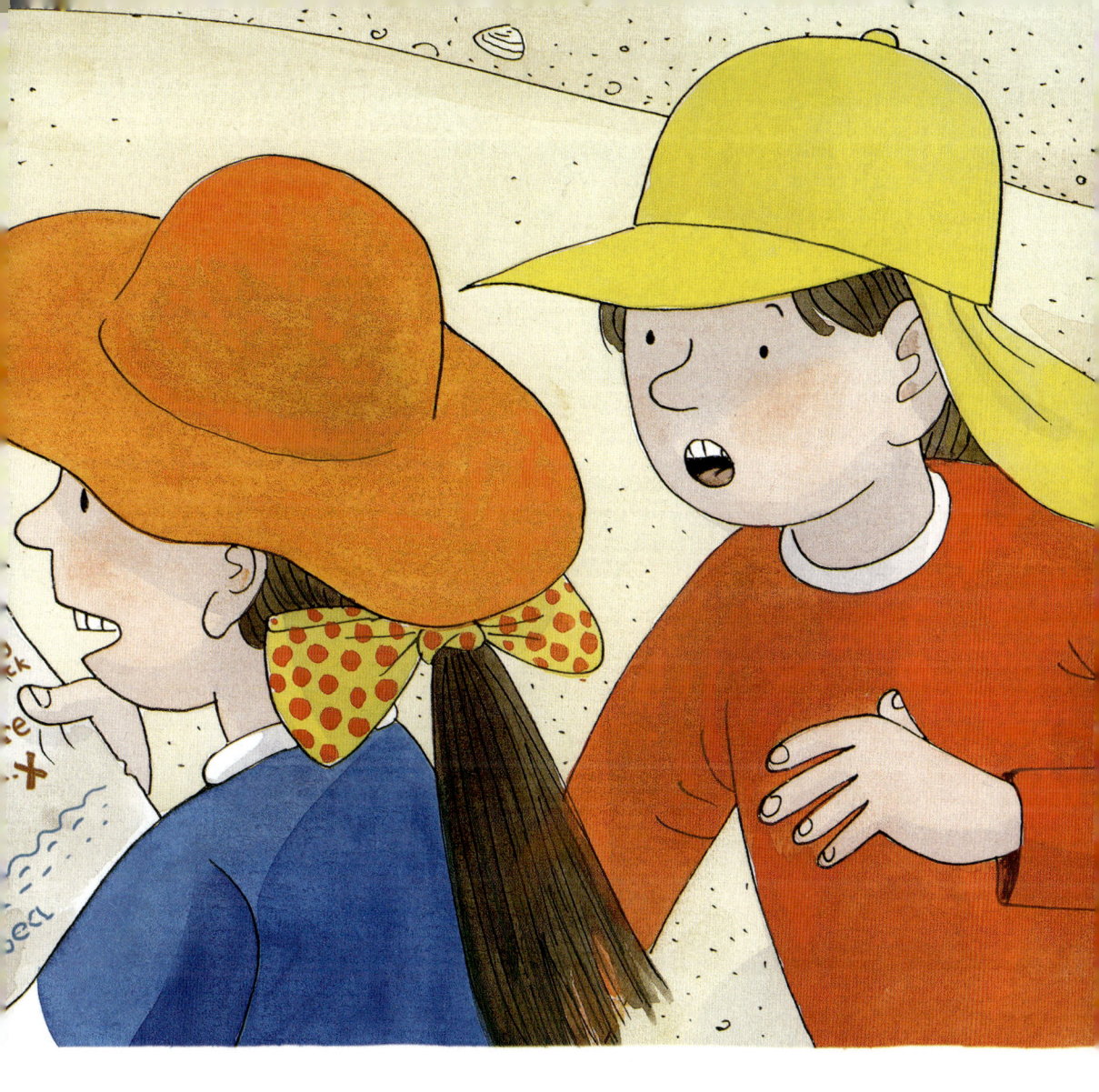

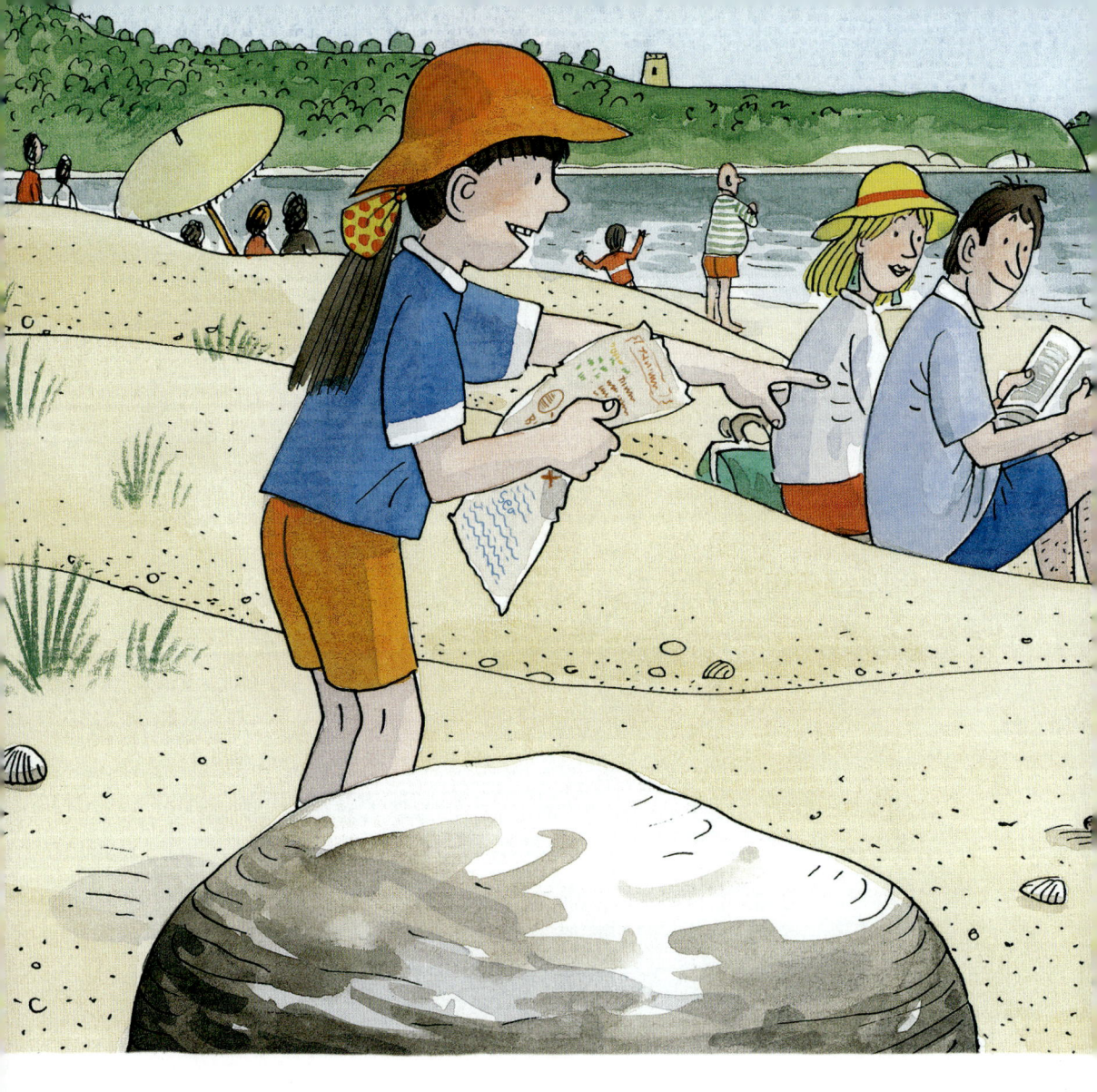

"Dig here," said Biff.

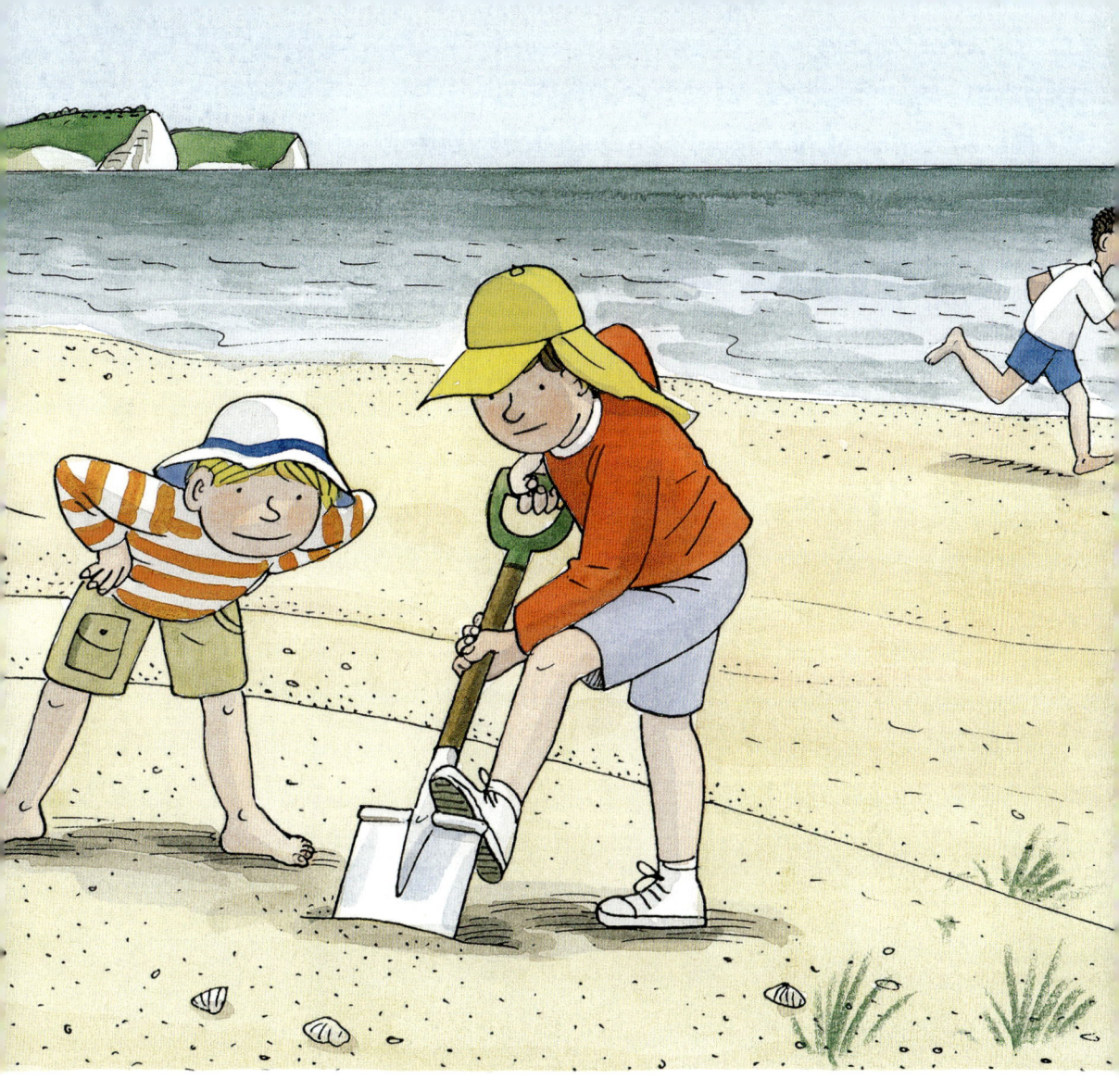

Chip dug in the sand.

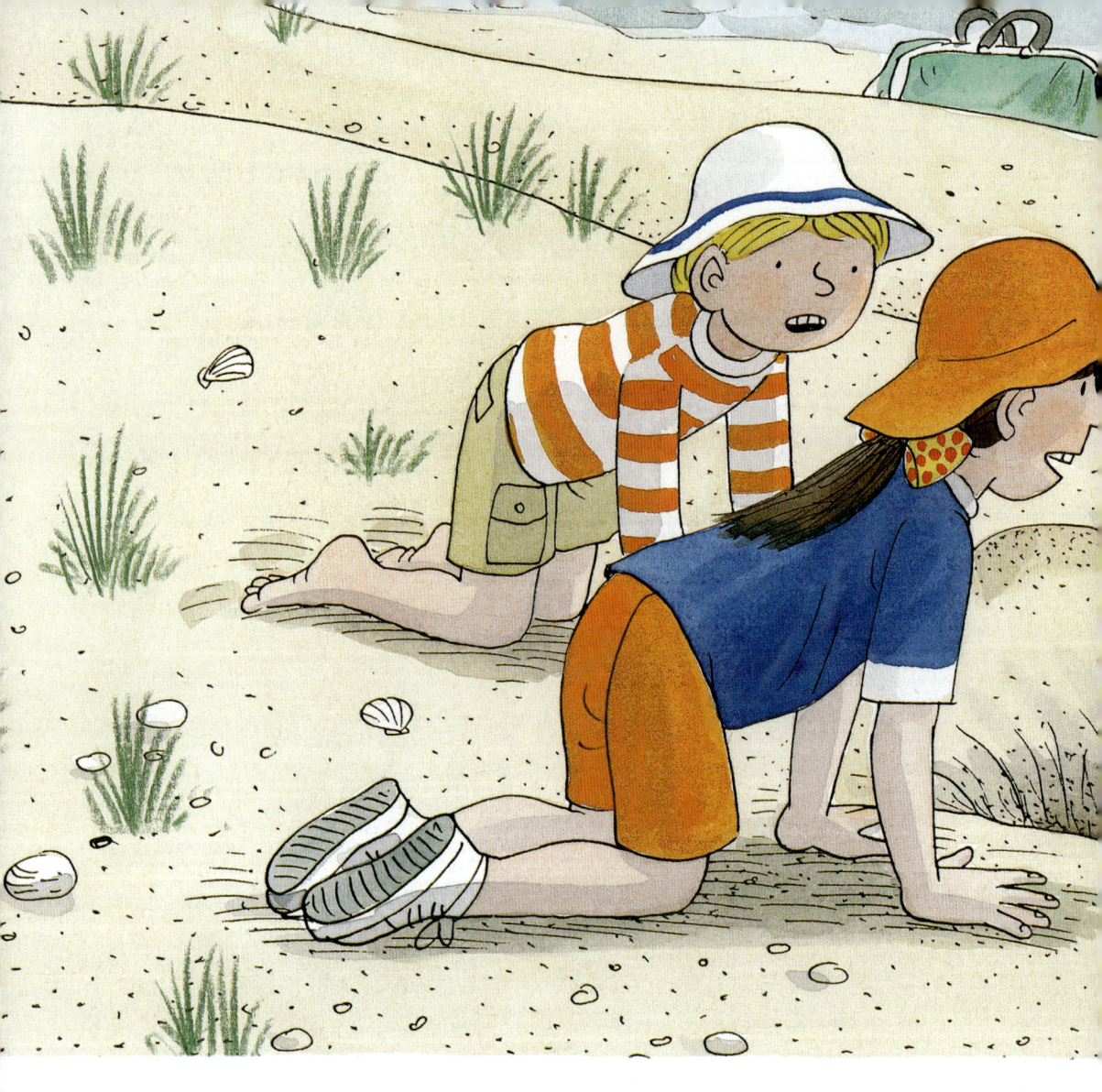

Chip found a box.

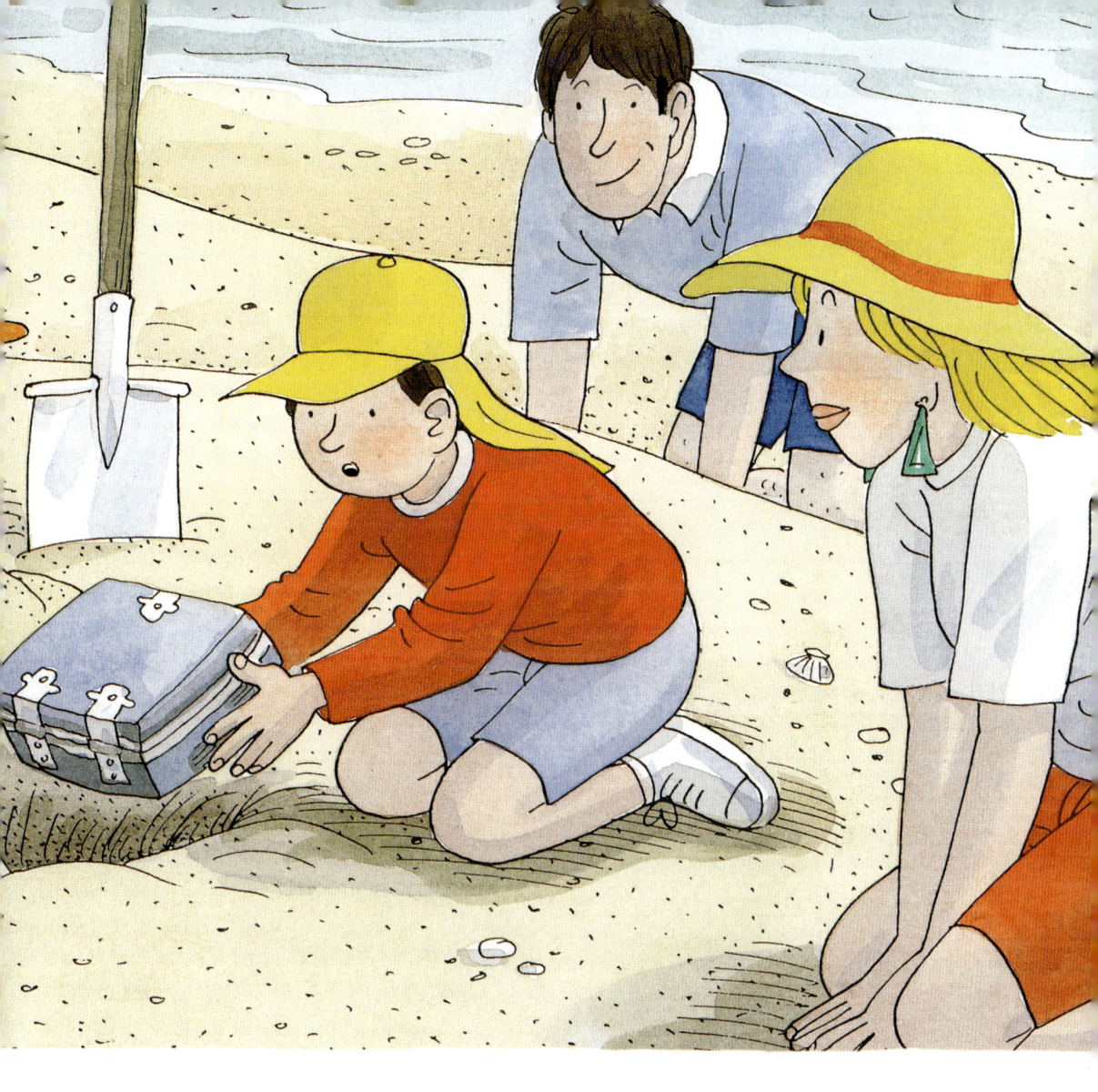

"Is it a box of treasure?" he said.

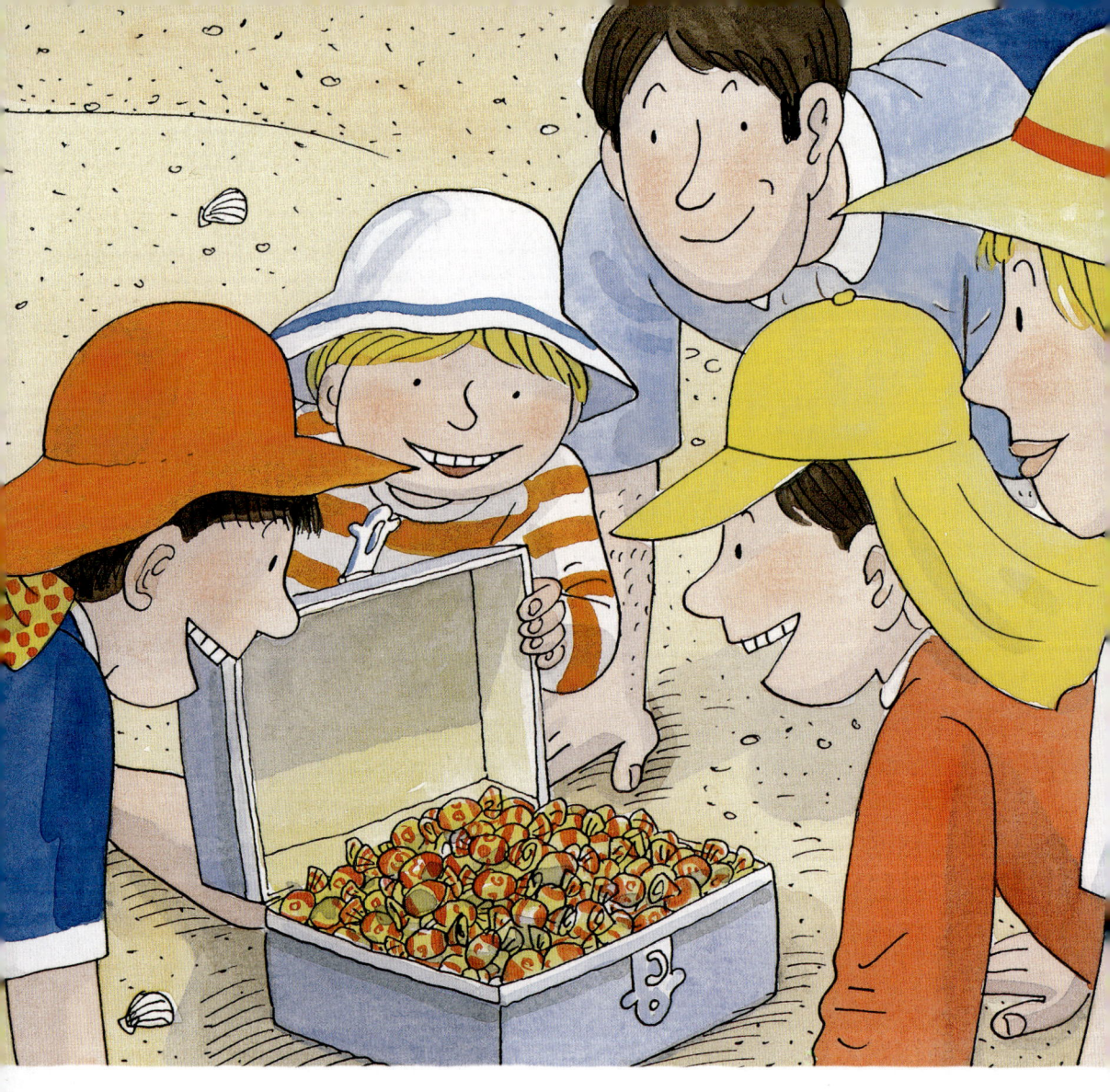

No. It was a box of sweets!